The Best Version of You:

Releasing Stress & Reclaiming
Your C.O.O.L. in Healthcare

2020 did a number on us healthcare workers! This book is dedicated to all of you as a token of my appreciation for your tireless work and efforts during this pandemic. A special thank you to my family and close friends for your unwavering love and support during my toughest times.

Love,

Ivette

Table of Contents

Introduction

Stress.

It's become a prevalent word in our current culture, not because the word is trendy or taken on a modern meaning, but because the effect it's having on us is seeping into every corner of our lives. Everyone is stressed these days, whether we work in corporate positions, work at home or are simply trying to manage a household. Even our kids are far more stressed than any previous generation on record.

As pervasive as this idea of stress has become, it's not something that we want to stick around. Most of us would do anything to eliminate the stress that we're feeling. Part of this is because modern stress is relentless and never seems to subside. It used to be that every once in a while, we got slammed with a stressful situation. We felt the heat as it ran its course, but eventually things would revert back to normal, and our regular life would continue. But no more.

Nowadays, stress shows up, and it stays. It's always fight or flight time, and our brains are constantly showered in the cocktail of hormones dispersed to deal with it. Unfortunately, our bodies were not designed for this, and as time passes more and more of us are realizing that something must be done. The question however, is what. We can't wave a wand and expect the world to shift into relaxation mode. Our computers, phones and tablets are not going to disappear. That means that the only course of action left to us is to train ourselves how to be more resilient and to deal with the stress coming our way more effectively.

A lot of the stress reduction techniques that exist out there are common sense. In fact, if we were less stressed, we might even think of them on our own. However, in the current climate, we often are not even aware that we have the power to do anything to get relief. We've almost come to point of accepting chronic, nagging stress as a way of life.

I'm here to remind you that a stressed life is not the only choice. We absolutely do have power to live life the way we want to live it. We don't have to constantly feel the fangs of stress puncturing our neck and draining away all of life force. Instead, we can reclaim our C.O.O.L. We can become impervious to the sort of stress that damages our spirit. Certain types of stress are good and healthy. They keep us on our toes, and we need it to get through challenging times. But life is not meant to be a permanent challenge. Eventually, we've got to feel the release of all that energy. We've got to learn how to better react to our environment and live a healthier, more fulfilling life.

If this idea intrigues you, and you're ready to learn more, turn the page and dig in

Welcome

In our current culture, stress has become prolific. Today's workforce is experiencing

job burnout and stress in epidemic proportions. Workers at all levels feel stressed out, insecure, and misunderstood. Many people feel the demands of the workplace, combined with the demands of home, have become too much to handle.

This is a bigger problem than you might think. As human beings, we are designed to handle stress in measured amounts. Our biochemistry responds to stressful events by flooding our bodies with chemicals that help us deal with the event we are facing. But in our modern, high-octane world, we have suddenly found ourselves in a position where stress never relents. Our jobs demand our attention at all hours of the day thanks to cell phones and remote working, and any stressor in our personal lives adds fuel to that fire.

The recent pandemic has exacerbated a problem that was already rampant in our society. When people began working from home, the boundaries between their work and personal lives became even more muddied than they already were. Now people were trying to manage two sets of responsibilities in a situation where there was no clear-cut difference between the two. They were constantly bombarded with an onslaught of demands coming from all directions.

If you were lucky enough to continue working outside of the home, the stressors increased with very little support from management to ease that burden. I was called into a hospital in New York in the early stages of the pandemic, and the complaints I heard there were similar to what I had heard in my hometown hospital in

Texas. People were stressed out from the intense schedules and overwhelming responsibilities at their job, but what was worse was that they had no support from the team around them. They felt unsupported and alone. This lack of support left them physically, mentally, and emotionally exhausted, and unable to do their job well with any consistency.

Seeing that this was not an isolated occurrence or just the result of poor management at one hospital, I knew I needed to address this issue. I know that stress can't simply be eliminated from our lives. We can't just wave a magic wand and clear away all sources of stress, but we most certainly can learn how to deal with stressors in a more productive fashion so that we're not succumbing to the pressures and breaking down from the weight of them.

Stress is our mental, physical, and behavioral response to something that could threaten our safety and wellbeing. Too much stress can result in serious physical, psychological, interpersonal, or performance problems. Too little stress, however, can also lead us to be unconcerned with getting on with things, including getting out of bed in the morning. So the question becomes, how can we effectively manage stress in our lives so that it empowers us rather than overwhelms us?

In addition to simply affecting the individual, stress also has s a significant impact on the organization. When the employees at an organization are routinely stressed and burnt out, it affects the patient care, morale and ultimately the bottom line. The stress is so intense in many instances that healthcare workers are leaving their jobs altogether, and they're not coming back. When employees start to leave at these higher rates, and the jobs can't be filled fast enough, the extra work shifts to the current staff, and they are already stressed to the breaking point themselves. When organizations add more responsibilities onto their existing workload without offering any form of support, the turnover cycle continues. Workers are leaving faster than they can be replaced and the current staff is picking up the slack. This cycle can only last for so long before it implodes. That's about where we are today.

In a stressed hospital culture, everybody suffers. The individual employees suffer, the patients suffer, and the organization suffers. Interestingly, however, there is very little being done to address the problem. Stress has mostly been viewed as a personal problem. The general outlook has always been that if you're feeling stressed or burnt out, it is your responsibility to handle it. If you can't handle it, then you're not cut out for the job. I'm of the mindset that stress management is an organizational concern. Much like an organization is responsible for training its workers to follow processes and procedures, it is also up to the organization to provide some support in how to deal with the high stress culture that comes with the job.

There are very simple steps that an organization can take that would transform the experience for their employees. It's really just about education. We can't eliminate stressors, but we can educate individuals to be more equipped to deal with those expected stressors. Preparation is half the battle.

However, as much as I am a proponent for change at the organizational level, I understand too, that we, as individuals can't wait for change to happen. We have to take things into our own hands, and start changing the landscape of our days so that we can live a fuller, more satisfying and more productive life. We want to excel and thrive at our jobs, and we want to enjoy our time off. There is room to both be an excellent employee who is managing all of her responsibilities efficiently and to have a healthy and full personal life.

That is what my book is all about. I'm going to teach you to take your health and wellness into your own hands. Your job may be stressful beyond repair, but it's not the stress that needs to be repaired. It's your outlook and approach to stress that needs to change. The C.O.O.L. method is a simple methodology that you can use to shift your thinking. When you use it religiously, you'll start to notice a significant difference. Work doesn't have to feel like an alternate reality where there is no time to even get lunch or make a call. And your personal life doesn't have to have the shadow of work hanging over it. There is a way to live a full and balanced life, and it's incredibly easy to access if you know what to focus on.

I will teach you healthy coping mechanisms that you can use in all areas of your life so that you're never feeling hopeless and overwhelmed again. When you put these into practice, your renewed mood and shift in attitude will rub off on those around you. Your co-workers will want to know how you manage the stress so well. The more of your department that can adopt this mentality, the better your daily work life will be, the better your patients will feel in your care, and the more efficient the department will run.

I invite you to forget what you know about work and what it should be, and to just be open to this alternative perspective. I assure you, you'll wonder why you never did these things sooner. If you're ready to finally get your stress under control, you are in the right place. Now let's get started.

The Temperature of the Current Nursing Climate

Nurses were burnt out and stressed in their roles before the pandemic, but COVID-19 has only taken a difficult situation and made it worse. COVID has "disrupted long-standing employment patterns and threatened nurses' financial, psychological and physical resilience."[1]

On the first level, you have nurses who are now emotionally depleted from continually dealing with the stress of dealing with a highly communicable disease. They've looked on helplessly as their patients succumbed to the disease while also gathering the reserve to come back into work the next day and do it again. They've tried to compartmentalize their fears for their own health as they worked to care for those in need. They've gone through many logistical changes and the implementation of various safety rules as the disease progressed, and we learned more about its spread. But all of this takes a heavy toll. Nurses were required to be in the thick of it every single day, and they weren't given tools or resources to deal with this new stress. Instead nurses were left to deal with these stresses on their own in whatever way they knew how. Not all of these methods were necessarily healthy, but all were understandable when you consider the levels of stress these nurses were under.

After the emotional and psychological stress, there was also physical distress. Many nurses ended up acquiring COVID-19 despite their precautions and protective measures. Dealing with and recovering from the disease adds another layer to the stress. It

---

[1] The Future of Nursing 2020-2030: Charting a Path to Achieve Health Equity. National Academy of Sciences.

has now become physical as nurses struggle with their breathing and other lingering physical symptoms. Even for the nurses who did not contract COVID-19, the repercussions of months of emotional stress takes its toll on the body in the form of muscle pain, soreness, fatigue and stress-induced illness. When a person is physically compromised in any way, it adds to their stress level. We are accustomed to a certain level of health, and when that is taken away, it affects our mental wellbeing in a perpetual cycle.

These problems are all exacerbated when hospital administrations decide that because of the drop off in revenue from private insurers during the pandemic, they will cut back in the most efficient way they know how. This means laying off and furloughing the majority of nursing staff. Not only does this create an additional financial component to the stress nurses are feeling, but the nurses remaining are responsible for twice the work in the absence of their co-workers. In an industry that was already comprised of too few nurses, hospitals and clinics are now creating an environment where there are insufficient nurses to handle the needs of the current patient-load.

Generally, the circumstances under which nurses operate are designed in a way that makes everything but the financial situation for the hospital exponentially worse. Nurses need better preparation for the varied circumstances that they will be expected to face and better support in the workplace. When nurses are overworked and pushed to the brink, they don't simply turn away from their responsibilities and try to escape the stress. They keep going. They internalize the stress that they are experiencing. They sacrifice their personal wellbeing in order that their patients are cared for. But this can only go on for so long before they eventually break.

The trouble is, that though many of the problems stem from the hospital and the current systems that are in place, very little is being done about it at an organizational level. We can't simply wait for change to take place and relieve us of our stressful situations. Instead, we must take ownership of the problem ourselves. This means taking responsibility for the stress that we, as nurses, are experiencing. There are obviously going to be many things that are out of our control, but we do have the ability to reduce our stress, to reclaim our wellbeing, and to implement measures that protect us from the negative effects of high-stress environments.

Within this book, I will show you how to take charge of your circumstances and become resilient in the face of stress. The future outlook of nurses post-pandemic is concerning. The baby boomers will retire and eventually require care of their own. New nurses are not entering the field at the rate they need to be in order to ensure care for everyone who will require it. There is no immediate relief on the horizon. That is why we must take things into our own hands. We can't allow the circumstances of the nursing industry to deter us from following our passion. But we also can't sacrifice ourselves in the effort to care for others. There has to be room for both.

This book is about showing you how to make room for both in your own life. It's only a small step in what is a much bigger problem, but it's a start, and it will drastically improve your personal experience in the nursing profession. I'm excited because it allows all of us to take ownership and make a change in the way we approach our jobs. If this intrigues you, keep reading and I'll share exactly what you need to be doing to improve the quality of your life.

Thoughts so far?

_____

_____

_____

_____

_____

_____

_____

_____

_____

_____

_____

_____

_____

_____

_____

_____

_____

_____

_____

_____

How Stressed Are You?

Before we get into learning how to deal with stress, let's first find out how stressed you are? There is a difference between being stressed and being burnt out. Sometimes stress is temporary. You might be dealing with a stressful situation at work or dealing with a life event that is taxing. If your stress passes when that situation ends, that's just the natural ebb and flow of stress, but if every event that occurs adds to your stress regardless of the intensity of the event itself, you are more likely suffering from burn out. This is the state of being stressed constantly with no relief, and this is when stress starts to have health repercussions.

How would you react to the below situations:

- A party where you wouldn't know many people

- A new job at a new company

- A move to another part of the country

- A 500-mile drive that takes you alone through some rather isolated country

- A trip to downtown Boston with friend where you are the driver

- A flight to Vancouver to attend a conference

- A dinner party for your spouses or partner's family

- An afternoon of holiday shopping at a large mall

On their own, these events are not particularly high stress events, but for someone with few resources on how to deal with stress, these can become stressors. You might read through this list and think that you would enjoy these activities, but for others they might be the source of great stress. When life is overwhelming on every front, adding something from this list might be the thing that puts you over the edge. Just the mere mention of it may send cause anxiety or panic. Using the C.O.O.L. system, I can teach you how to approach events like these and others from a more positive standpoint so that big tasks don't automatically become stressful tasks.

Imagine being in the following scenario:

You're at work, and it's almost 4:30pm. You have two top-priority deadlines to meet today, and it is your turn to pick up your child from the babysitter no later than 6pm. You find yourself going form one project to another and getting very little accomplished. Everyone else has their own time pressures so you can't delegate any part of your work to anyone else. Your manager is breathing down your neck, and you feel the muscles in your shoulders and neck beginning to tighten, signaling the onset of another tension headache. How will you cope?

A situation like the one above is very difficult to deal with when you don't have the right resources, and you're already taxed to your breaking point. Depending on your current state, you can react in two entirely different ways. It might be a simple fix if you are in a good space, but if you're on the brink, this could be just the type of event that throws you into a downward spiral.

The goal of this book is to teach you how to deal with unexpected issues such as this with ease and coolness. When you approach any problem from the right mindset, you are better able to handle adversity. Since we can't change the stressful events, the only option is to change our approach.

Let's dig in a little deeper into your stress levels.

On a scale of 1-10, how would you rate your current stress levels?

On a scale of 1-10, what would a healthy level of stress feel like?

On a scale of 1-10, how much of your energy do you spend worrying about events in the past?

On a scale of 1-10, how much of your energy do you spend worrying about events in the future?

How often do you use the phrase, "I'm so stressed out." What are some of the reasons that cause you to feel this way?

Does your stress keep you up at night?

Does your stress prevent you from enjoying free time with friends or family?

Is your stress affecting your health? If so, to what degree and how often?

Is your stress affecting your ability to your job well?

How often do you feel relief from your stress, if at all?

What have been the major stressors in your life over the past year? Two years?

What are the ways you've tried to reduce or resolve your stress in the past?

_____

_____

_____

_____

_____

_____

_____

_____

_____

_____

_____

_____

_____

_____

_____

_____

_____

_____

_____

_____

_____

_____

_____

_____

_____

_____

What to do now

These questions are a way for you to review your current situation. As you go through your answers, you'll have opportunity to address the way stress shows up in your life.

According to research done by Holmes and Rahe in the Journal of Psychosomatic Research, chronic stress plays a significant role in health. Their research demonstrated that the more stressful events you encountered in a 24-month period, the more likely you were to become ill.

Stressors act as stimuli that evoke a certain response in our bodies. When this happens, we must adapt in some way. The disparity between the demands we are experiencing and the resources that that we have at our disposal will determine how we react to that stress. That is why having more resources reduces the severity of the perceived stress.

Some stressors are small, like finding out that there is no toilet paper in the bathroom or calling someone to find that their voicemail is full. As we move up that scale, we may find things getting stuck far from home, or being the victim of a crime. The biggest stressors can be severe events like natural disasters, acts or war and dangerous riots. No matter what the magnitude of the stressor is, we need to have tools in our arsenal with which to address these events. When we don't have these resources, we are forced to deal with the events often in ways that we've been taught through our culture and society. Many of these ways are a way of avoiding the cause of the stress, and can include turning to drugs, alcohol or food. These are unhealthy tools to use to combat stress, and can easily turn into bigger problems that add to the stress rather than reducing it.

Events over which we have very little control, which occur suddenly and unpredictably, and which span long periods of time, generally have the biggest impact on physical and emotional health. In addition, even small events that are chronically repeated over a long period of time (like a colleague being late for work every day for a prolonged period) can be equally taxing. The question then becomes, how can you operate from a place of empowerment when it comes to things you cannot control. That's a big question, but involves an element of flexibility and openness, which we will discuss in the upcoming chapters. By the end of this experience, you will know exactly how to stand strong against unpredictable stressors without feeling that you've given away your control.

Before we start to get into the strategy, I want you to know that being stressed is not a bad thing. You don't have to feel guilty that you've gotten yourself into a stressed or burnt out state, and don't know how to get out of it. Stress reduction is not something that we're taught in school or in our training for any job. Many times stress is worn like a badge of honor where the individuals that are most stressed are seen as the most productive and efficient at their jobs. This should not be the goal. Stress does not equate success.

From my perspective, being stressed is the false goal that has been put into place in our non-stop, "always on" culture. I want to squash this notion. We can be effective at our jobs without sacrificing our sanity and wellbeing. And I argue, that we can be even more productive when we approach our life with a C.O.O.L. mindset. Stressed is how we feel when we aren't managing the circumstances life is throwing at us well. When we are in a C.O.O.L. mindset, no longer matters what life throws at us, because we are prepared to handle everything. To me, that's a much greater place to be than simply wishing things would ease up.

The goal is to live our life with purpose, and when you get the jump on stress, you will be better positioned to do so.

Now that we understand what stress is and what are stress levels are, it's time to figure out what exactly we can do about it.

_____

_____

_____

_____

_____

_____

_____

_____

_____

_____

_____

_____

_____

_____

_____

_____

_____

_____

_____

_____

C – Comprehend

Understand the Factors that Cause Stress

Before we can begin to combat stress, we must first understand how it's caused. Stress is typically triggered by an external event or occurrence. Our body then responds to this stimulus by having a physiological response. A triggered person might experience the arousal of the sympathetic nervous system, a flood of stress hormones being released into their bloodstream, muscle tension, increased heart rate and over time an increased susceptibility to illness and disease. Once these physiological symptoms are present, the mind reacts. This can be expressed as worry, excess excitement, low self-confidence, hopelessness or anticipation. After that, exacerbating factors determine the severity and degree of the experienced stress. These factors include the intensity and duration of the event, how manageable the experience is and whether the occurrence will repeat regularly or not.

Although stress is responsible for many of the prevalent illnesses we struggle with today, stress is not a virus or bacteria. On its own, stress is actually not dangerous. It only becomes dangerous when we don't manage it the right way. Often people feel stressed because their body is experiencing the physiological symptoms and the mind is reacting with uncomfortable responses. The chain reaction can cause people to avoid important tasks, shirk responsibility or descend into disorganization. It might even prompt people to seek a numbing solution like drugs or alcohol. But all of these responses are unhealthy reactions to stress. If you can comprehend what's actually at play in your body and you can choose to react differently to the stressful circumstances around you.

It might help at this point to remember that stress is often an exhilarating and positive experience. Sometimes when we're in a more positive or stronger state of mind, stress lands much differently. Imagine packing for a vacation. Often planning to go away and even being away can be highly stressful experiences, but that stress is mitigated by the fact that we're on vacation. We deal with vacation stressors differently than if we were tasked with the same amount of tasks at our job. We experience the rush of stress hormones as excitement rather than worry and we're happy to deal with it all because we'll be on a beach in Bali shortly.

The stress itself is essentially the same; it's only our perspective that is different. Stress on its own is a neutral experience. We are in control of how we allow it to affect our lives, and this is always true – not just when we're dealing with something that we're excited about. When we can understand this, we no longer have to fear stress or particular stressors. Instead, we understand that its just about cultivating effective ways of dealing with stress so that we don't get lost in the negative cognitive responses that our physiological changes might lead us to.

I often hear people describe this modern era as being more stressful than previous decades. This might be true. We certainly have access to a lot more news and alerts at all hours of the day. Our networks are larger and our technology is more advanced. But we also have a considerable advantage over previous generations in that we can leverage technology to help outsmart stress. We can use technology to help us stay organized, to automate many monotonous parts of our life and to make many tasks easier. So we are not living in an unfortunate time where we simply have to adapt to more stress. We have the tools to deal with stress better than ever before if we take advantage of them. We are always in control of how stress lands on us. And if we learn how to better absorb these stressful events, we can live a happier, healthier life. The current technological world that we live in could help us to live a more balanced life if we just let it.

Now that we Comprehend what stress is and how it works, we can begin to cultivate the qualities that stress can't permeate. We can become resilient to the stressors and arm ourselves with coping mechanisms that actually make a difference.

Journal Prompts:

- What your biggest sources of stress?

- How do you react when you're stressed?

- What are you unable to do when you're feeling stressed or overwhelmed?

- What do you feel in times high stress? How do you express those emotions?

- Is there someone who you take your stress out on?

- Has your health suffered at all due to stress?

- How do you currently cope with stress? What methods work and what don't?

O – Openness

Are you Flexible?

Openness is all about being flexible. When we are flexible, it makes change easier to cope with. By eliminating the rigidity in our lives, we are suddenly more open and accepting of our surrounds, meaning that stress has less power to disrupt our lives.

Much of the negativity associated with stress comes because have a certain expectation of things should go. When things don't go according to plan, we get stressed. This can be as simple as missing our plane or getting interrupted during our work day so that we don't finish our work. In these cases, the stress of external life lands on us in a way that makes us more anxious, aggravated and upset. It doesn't help us achieve; instead it feels like an obstacle in the way of our success.

Similarly stress can act as a motivator in other circumstances. Say we are hosting a bachelorette weekend. There is a lot to coordinate and ample opportunity for things to go wrong, but when our mood is energized and positive, the stress of having all these things line up perfectly gives us energy and inspires us to overcome the obstacles rather than acting as a hindrance. This might be viewed much differently if you look at it from the perspective of the bride versus that of the maid of honor. The bride might view the stress negatively because she desperately wants everything to go perfectly, whereas the Maid of Honor is more open. She is less concerned with the exact outcome and more concerned with solving the problems as they come up and achieving the best result. She has more flexibility. This doesn't mean that her flexibility will ruin the weekend due to unforeseen challenges. It just means that she will be better able to deal with those unexpected events than the bride who has very specific expectations.

Being flexible allows us to go with the flow and avoid the negative effects of stress. It's similar to how a tree bends with the wind. If trees were rigid, they would snap in a strong breeze. Instead trees move and bend ever so subtly so that they become impervious to the wind. They are stronger do the fact they are flexible. They let the wind bend them a bit, and then the stress of heavy winds doesn't automatically break them. It's important for us to take on these characteristics if we want to live a more calm and peaceful life.

When you are faced with criticism, listen to the feedback. When someone treats you unfairly, ask yourself what could be going on with them to have caused them to act that way. When someone is pushing you in a certain direction, don't blindly fight, but lean into what they are saying. You might learn something new or discover a new possibility. But you won't ever find out if you move through the world with rigidity.

It might be tempting to imagine a world without stress in it at all. Then you wouldn't need to be open and flexible, you could just go about your business without the stressors that you currently face. Interestingly, the absence of stress is not the solution. Without stress, our lives become boring and uneventful. Everything has the same level of urgency – which is none. As much as you might be stressed at work, you look forward to the reprieve on Friday night as you anticipate the fun weekend you have planned. How fun would that weekend be if your entire week was bland and uneventful. There would be no contrast between work and fun. When everything is consistently low-key, we get bored. Experience boredom long enough and you'll just be left with fatigue.

Picture yourself sitting in a empty for an hour. There are no windows, no devices or televisions to entertain you – just four bare walls and simple chair to sit in. The temperature is perfect. You are neither hot nor cold. You are comfortable, and you've got no responsibilities to worry about. Everything is taken care of. This is a room where there is no stress. This is what you've been wishing for, for the stress in your life to disappear. Now you've got it. All you have to do is sit in the chair and relax indefinitely.

As you can see, taking away stress does not solve the problem. Sure, you no longer have stress, but your life has not improved in any way. My point is that we need stress in our lives. That's what makes life interesting. However, we cannot let stress take over our lives and impact them negatively, affecting our health and wellbeing. The thing that makes stress manageable is how we interact with it. Being open is a big part of how we can deal with the various stressors in our life in a more effective way.

Take some time to think about the most stressful moments in your life. If you had been more open in these moments, could you have experienced those circumstances differently? Really brainstorm here. Allow yourself to imagine other outcomes. Don't focus on the fact that you might've been too rigid in these moments or that you did do the best you could. The past is what is, and you can't change it. This exercise is merely to envision the ways in which being more open could have opened other doors. When you do this with events in your past and see other potential outcomes, you'll be more likely to embrace being in flexible in future circumstances.

There is a freedom in cultivating openness. You are no longer tied to specific outcomes and can allow the story of your life to unfold in more spontaneous fashion. This might sound scary or unappealing to some of you, but I urge you to give this a try. When you are open, you allow for possibility, and possibility is where the best part of life is. We can't always foresee or plan the best outcomes. We must allow nature to show us the things we might miss. When you can embrace openness, you will not only relive the negative effects of stress, you will also discover paths available to you and qualities within you that you never knew were there.

Journal Prompts:

- Do you go into circumstances and situations with high expectations? What happens when those are not met?

- Are you more flexible with other people as opposed to yourself? If so, how can you extend that allowance to yourself?

- What are some stressful events that you've experienced? How could those moments have gone differently if you had been more flexible at those times?

- Can you think of a time when stress actually motivated you to do better or gave you more energy? Describe why you think that is?

- What does negative stress feel like? Why do you think you the stress affected you like this?

Time for Notes:

_____

_____

_____

_____

_____

_____

_____

_____

_____

_____

_____

_____

_____

_____

_____

_____

_____

_____

_____

_____

_____

O – Outlets

Relaxation, Reset, Release

In our busy lives, it's absolutely vital to have outlets where we can get away from the stressors that are pressing us. Whether that stress is good or bad, we still need places and periods of time where we can decompress and reset. Many things are constantly happening around us, to us and adjacent to us, and we need to allow our bodies and minds the opportunity to let those things go.

When we see stress take its toll on people, we often find a person who never took a break. They may have known how to relax but they never actually prioritized relaxation into their schedule. If this is you, I encourage you to take a step back and allow yourself these vital outlets. None of us can do this thing called life on our own with no intervention, no break and no reprieve. But somehow, we've come to believe that the more we do without a break, the stronger or more empowered we are. This is not true. It's simply a recipe for burnout.

In reality, the most successful and satisfied people, don't have easier lives. They just know how to check out from what is going on in those lives in healthy and productive ways. We give this type of advice to our children all the time. When they have a big test at school that they've been studying all week for, we tell them to stop studying and get some sleep. They already know everything. All they need is a good night's rest and they'll ace the test. If they've have a big basketball game the next day, we make sure they eat a good meal and go to bed early. We don't tell them that they ought to wear themselves down practicing until their muscles hurt and they can't keep their eyes open. Yet for some reason, we assume this technique is best when it comes to ourselves. We work ourselves to the bone. We stay late at work. We answer work emails even when we would rather be paying attention to family. We push ourselves to our limit, and we don't even consider taking a break.

Outlets are necessary not only to our success but to our wellbeing. Without proper outlets, we are attaching ourselves to a ticking time bomb, and eventually that bomb is going to go off. It's not a question of, "if," it is only "when." The good part is that we can avoid that bomb by simply incorporating some healthy outlets into our daily lives. These are easy things to do. They don't require elaborate plans that will add more stress to your day. They are simple things that anyone can do with a little effort. The only requirement is that you make the time to do them regularly.

Here are some outlets you can start incorporating into your day immediately:

- Breathe – This is the easiest one. You have everything you need to do this at any moment in time. If thing start to feel overwhelming, take five minutes and sit outside with your eyes closed just breathing – big, deep inhales and exhales. Feel the breath moving in and out of your lungs. Try to push all other thoughts out of your mind and focus only on your breath. There are medical reasons why this is helpful. It increase oxygen to your brain and synchronizes your heart rate to your breath, releasing endorphins that have a natural calming effect. It also helps to rid the body of toxins.

- Listen to Music – Music has the ability to transport us. It takes us to another place and time, and can elevate our mood. Make a playlist of some of your favorite songs, songs that make you feel inspired or fill you with joy. When the day seems to be getting away from you, take a walk around the block while you listen. This small act can have powerful effects.

- Exercise – Moving your body releases endorphins, the feel-good hormones so you'll not only create benefits for your body, but for you mental state as well. The exercise can be as simple as walking or you can do something that you enjoy. Yoga, cycling, swimming or even dance all count.

- Immerse Yourself in Water – By this I mean either taking a shower, which can be invigorating and get charged up for your day or indulge in a bath, which is more relaxing and restorative. You might start your day with a shower and end it with bath. Take a book or some music with you and shut the door. Take this time to recharge and restore.

- Give and Receive a Massage – Massages are great ways to relax. You can always splurge and treat yourself to a professional massage or you can teach your partner how to give you massage and take turns.

- Spend Time in Nature – Make time to walk in the park, go for a hike or sit by a stream. You can even spend some uninterrupted time in your backyard. Let nature heal you. Listen to the birds, stare at the clouds and smell the fragrances. You can also take a more active approach and garden or tend to the yard. Just make sure that the time is restorative and enjoyable.

The bottom line is that having healthy outlets is important. When you properly take of yourself in this way, you will be better able to show up fully in other areas of your life. When you run yourself ragged, you are doing everyone a disservice. By treating yourself to some healthy relaxation and release, you will ensure that you're showing up as your best self in everything you do.

Journal Prompts:

- What do you typically do to relax? How often do you indulge?

- Do you feel guilty when you partake in various forms of relaxation. Why is that?

- When you have experience moments of relaxation, how did you feel afterwards?

- Where can you make time for some of these outlets?

_____

_____

_____

_____

_____

_____

_____

_____

_____

_____

_____

_____

_____

_____

_____

_____

L – Love

Relationships

The final piece in the releasing stress is achieved by sharing your burdens with others. I don't mean that you should simply vent to everyone you encounter about your difficult day. I mean that you should focus on cultivating and building strong relationships and friendships so that you have people around you to provide support and encouragement when you need it most. When we try to live our lives in a vacuum, attempting to handle everything on our own, we inadvertently cause ourselves more stress. We fool ourselves into believe that others don't care or that we are a burden, when in reality, we are stronger in numbers.

It's important to form relationships at your job, at your children's school and in your community so that you can not only share in the good and fun things that come up but so that you someone to turn to when you are overwhelmed, confused or scared. I can't express the importance of relationships enough. Even if you feel strong and on top of the world right now, you won't always feel that way. Life is a constant rollercoaster of ups and downs, and having healthy relationships helps us navigate those highs and lows.

There are plenty of ways to reach out and connect to those around you. Try just being friendly to the people around you. Offer to help for nothing in return. People generally like to help those who have shown them kindness in the past; and they don't tend to forget that sort of thing. Giving support is reciprocal. Support them, and they will support you. Get acquainted with your neighbors. Take an interest in their wellbeing and do kind things. If you see that their garbage can blew out into the road, walk it back for them. There are many simple ways to engage that cost you very little, but these same people could turn out to great resources in stressful times.

Imagine you've been held up at work late, and you are the only home that week to let out the dog. You get a call from your Mom about something urgent you need to go and handle, and when you're finally on the way home, there is an accident on the highway. All of these things are adding stress to an already stressful day. You're worried about getting back to the dog, but there is nothing you can do about it. If you're on good terms with your neighbor, you can save yourself hours of stress by making a simple phone call once you knew you needed to stay late at work. That's just one way in which sharing the load relieves stress. We are not meant to live solitary lives and rely on ourselves for everything. We are social creatures, and we work and live better when we share responsibility. By building strong relationships, you are building a tribe that will help navigate these choppy seas.

In addition, it's also very important to learn that it's okay to ask for help. As women, especially, we often feel that there is shame in asking for help. We believe that we have to do things on our own in order to be deemed worthy or perhaps because we know we can do things better. But it's also vital to be able to delegate, and to ask others for assistance when we are pushed to our max. There is no weakness in asking for help. And to be honest, sometimes I think it even takes more strength to ask for help than to continue pressing on. You help all involved when you ask for help. By trying to do things all on your own, you compromise yourself, but you also risk letting others down because you don't have the time or resources to dedicate the thing. You're stretching yourself too thin. At first, it might seem like you're superwoman as you blow through all your tasks, but no one can keep that up indefinitely. Eventually, the tears begin to show in the fabric. Things get forgotten, projects are down halfway, and you become exhausted. Instead, just know your own limits, and know when to say, "no."

You can see how important good relationships are in overall wellbeing, and the same thing is true for the relationship with yourself. It's important that your relationship with yourself is maintained and cared for. This means not degrading yourself for making a mistake, not overworking yourself with no breaks, being affirming with yourself when you do something right, and overall treating yourself with respect and dignity. Sometimes we find that it's easier to treat others well, but when it comes to how we talk to ourselves, anything goes. We berate, criticize and talk down to ourselves so that we feel badly and are unable to do good work. Do what you can to make positivity a habit in your self-talk. Encourage yourself as if you were your own best friend. In a way, you are. You'll be amazed at what comes when you have a positive self-view.

Be aware too of your inner voice. Oftentimes our gut tells us a lot about what is right and wrong. We know instinctively when we're making a good decision and when we're forcing something that isn't right. Take the time to listen to your inner voice. Don't discount it as nothing. Learn to trust your gut. Oftentimes, your gut will steer you away from stressful situations. Sometimes, it's when we follow too closely to obligation or responsibility that we find ourselves in stressful situations that we'd never be in if we just did what we knew was right at the start. Learn to tune into this voice and trust it.

Journal Prompts:

- Do you have strong relationships in your life? Do you use these relationships as a source of support and encouragement? Elaborate.

- Do you often feel like you have to do things on your own? Do you feel guilty reaching out for help?

- How inclined are you to help others in their times of strife? How does it make you feel? If it makes you feel good, wouldn't you want to give others this opportunity to help you?

- Are there certain places in your life where you don't have any friends or acquaintances? Are these places more stressful than other areas? How could you make more friends here?

Ivette Palomeque

Conclusion

Managing stress is not about eliminating stress from our lives. Not only is that an impossible task, it also doesn't entirely serve us because as we've discussed some stress is good. It motivates us, excites us and propels us forward. The real trick to beating stress for good is to simply shift our thinking and restructure our lives in a way that negative stress doesn't send us into a tailspin.

When we can Comprehend what's causing our stress, Open ourselves up to alternative possibilities, and find healthy Outlets, and cultivate sources of Love in all areas of our life, we will be better positioned to deal with any of the troubling stressors that come our way.

It's similar to being on a boat. The ocean waves can be a violent and damaging force, but we wouldn't just stay on land because of it. We would just be sure to navigate it on a boat that was built well and strong. After all sometimes there is nothing greater than to be lying on a boat while listening to the waves hit the bow. But you would also want to be protected when those waves get stronger, and a storm starts brewing. If your boat is secure, strong waves won't have much effect.

The same is true for stress. When we make ourselves resilient, we become impervious to the stress. Yes, the stress still strikes us, but it doesn't knock us down. That's the difference between living a stressful life versus reclaiming you and keeping your C.O.O.L.

This is obviously only the tip of the iceberg. There is much to learn about handling stress and building up your reserves so that you are best equipped to handle life's biggest stressors. To learn more, please contact me at www.FrontlineLife.co

About the Author

Ivette Palomeque, BSN RN is an Advocate. From the hospitality industry to a Registered Nurse working in ICUs, Level 1 Trauma Centers, and COVID-19 units, has a deep understanding of the trials nurses face on every front.

After spending more than a decade in ICUs and over a year caring for patients in COVID-19 units, Ivette knows what helps prevent burnout in healthcare, keeps frontliners motivated, and drives nurses to be the most trusted professionals.

She takes pride in helping nurses navigate the frontlines and founded Frontline Life Media and Frontline Life Healthcare Club as an exclusive support group and safe space for nurses to connect -- nurse-to-nurse and human-to-human. She takes pride in providing nurses with resources and thrives on connecting nurses as human first and nurses second.

Ivette has landed media coverage in print and broadcast outlets around the internationally including CNN (espanol), CNBC, ABC and CBS. Sharing her experience as a frontline nurse during COVID-19, Palomeque also uses her nursing leadership experience to train nurse leaders and nurses on wellness, mental health, advocacy, and more.

In addition to her extensive nursing experience, Ivette is fluent in both English and Spanish and has extensive experience in the hospitality industry which means she serves with a very strong commitment to stellar customer service.

Notes

Notes

Made in the USA
Coppell, TX
13 April 2022

76508600R00028